Back to Basics

MATHS

for 10-11 year olds

BOOK ONE

George Rodda

Addition and subtraction

32 star players have entered this competition.

 Fill in this table showing the number of players for each round and the number of matches.

Round	1	2	3	Semi-final	Final
Number of players	32	16			
Number of matches	16			2	1

What was the total number of matches played? ☐

How many matches would be needed altogether

for an entry of 64 players? ☐

 Find these totals.

639	499	609	746
+471	+501	+391	+284
———	———	———	———

 Work out these differences.

431	507	600	987
−229	−409	−237	−789
———	———	———	———

Fill in the total for each of these players.

Player	Alan	Betty	Chris	Don	Edith
Score for round 1	141	302	237	402	363
Score for round 2	52	109	143	299	237
Total					

 Fill in the missing score for each player.

Player	Fred	Gill	Heidi	Ian	Jo	Kim
Score	300	299	301	291	259	249
Needed to make 500	200					
Total	500	500	500	500	500	500

 Find the total and write down how many more
are needed to make 400.

```
      60           100          120           25
     140            20          120           15
 +   101        +    2        +   5        +    4
 _____        _____        _____        _____

 _____        _____        _____        _____
```

Score needed: ☐   ☐   ☐   ☐

 For each of these sums write in two of the
numbers **4, 5, 6, 7** to make the sum correct.

```
     7 ☐          ☐ 6          4 ☐          7 ☐
 +   ☐ 4      +   5 ☐      +   ☐ 7      +   ☐ 4
 _____      _____      _____      _____
 1 3 0        1 0 3        1 2 2        1 3 9
```

```
     ☐ 6          7 ☐          ☐ 5          ☐ 4
 -   5 ☐      -   ☐ 5      -   4 ☐      -   5 ☐
 _____      _____      _____      _____
   2 2          3 1          1 8          1 8
```

Multiplication

In 3 years this cow should give

```
   1500
×     3
────────
   4500 litres of milk.
```

 At the rate of 1500 litres of milk a year for each cow, fill in this table:

Number of cows	1	2	3	4	5
Number of litres in 1 year	1500				

 Now fill in this table using the rate of 1500 litres a year for each cow.

Milk given by	1 cow	2 cows	
in 1 year	1500		litres
in 2 years			litres
in 3 years			litres
in 4 years		12000	litres

 Work out these multiplication sums.

```
   1500          1500          1500          1500
×     5        ×     6       ×     7       ×     8
──────         ──────        ──────        ──────

──────         ──────        ──────        ──────
```

    125×3   126×3   123×6   222×5

=   =   =   =

```
    205              178              420              199
×     9          ×     8          ×     5          ×     9
─────            ─────            ─────            ─────

─────            ─────            ─────            ─────
```

 Fill in this multiplication square.

×	1	2	3	4	5	6	7	8	9	10
1										
2			6							
3										
4						24				
5										
6										
7										
8										
9										
10										

The answers in the box belong to the sums below.

```
        860                    747

               1836

        2919                  1827

               4527

        1476                  2160
```

 Put the answers in the right place.

```
      172              270              203              249
×       5          ×       8          ×       9          ×       3
─────            ─────            ─────            ─────

─────            ─────            ─────            ─────


      306              492              503              417
×       6          ×       3          ×       9          ×       7
─────            ─────            ─────            ─────

─────            ─────            ─────            ─────
```

Division

This piggy bank is full of coins.
It has 240 one penny coins in it.

Ian, Emma and Mary
share the money.

They have 240p ÷ 3 = 80p each.

 From 240p:
how many children could have

How many could have 50p

and how much would be left?

10p each? ☐

5p each? ☐

20p each? ☐

40p each? ☐

☐ children

☐ p

 Finish these division sums.

$4\overline{)84}$ $3\overline{)84}$ $6\overline{)84}$ $7\overline{)84}$

$4\overline{)840}$ $5\overline{)840}$ $6\overline{)840}$ $7\overline{)840}$

$2\overline{)840}$ $3\overline{)840}$ $8\overline{)840}$ $10\overline{)840}$

$2\overline{)804}$ $3\overline{)804}$ $6\overline{)804}$ $6\overline{)408}$

Write down the answer and the remainder.

$2\overline{)50}$ rem __O__ $4\overline{)50}$ rem ____ $6\overline{)50}$ rem ____

$2\overline{)500}$ rem ____ $4\overline{)500}$ rem ____ $6\overline{)500}$ rem ____

$50 \div 10$ $50 \div 8$ $50 \div 3$

$=$ ____ rem ____ $=$ ____ rem ____ $=$ ____ rem ____

$500 \div 10$ $500 \div 8$ $500 \div 3$

$=$ ____ rem ____ $=$ ____ rem ____ $=$ ____ rem ____

The divisors of 14 are 1, 2, 7 and 14.

 Fill in the missing divisors.

27 is divisible by   1, 3, ____, 27

25 is divisible by   1, ____, 25

28 is divisible by   1, ____, ____, ____, 14, 28

24 is divisible by   1, ____, ____, ____, ____, ____, ____, 24

36 is divisible by   1, ____, ____, ____, ____, ____, ____, ____, 36

29 is divisible by   ____, ____

 Work out the answers to these divisions.
Some of them have remainders.

$275 \div 5$ $275 \div 6$ $275 \div 7$

$=$ _____ $=$ _____ $=$ _____

$207 \div 4$ $632 \div 5$ $900 \div 8$

$=$ _____ $=$ _____ $=$ _____

$640 \div 6$ $891 \div 9$ $1011 \div 10$

$=$ _____ $=$ _____ $=$ _____

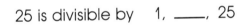

Graphs

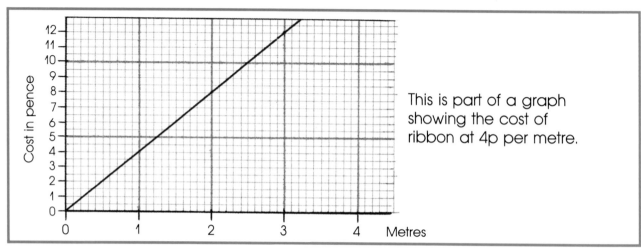

This is part of a graph showing the cost of ribbon at 4p per metre.

 At 4p per metre:

2 metres will cost ___ p   3 metres will cost ___ p

2½ metres will cost ___ p   1½ metres will cost ___ p

Use the graph to check your answers.

Mary can peel potatoes at the rate of
20 potatoes in 40 minutes.

 At this rate of peeling how long will it take to peel

10 potatoes? _____ minutes

30 potatoes? _____ minutes

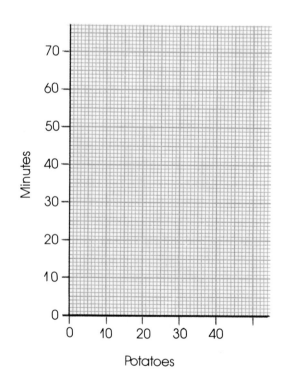

 On this graph draw a line showing Mary's time taken to peel potatoes.

What is the average time taken by Mary to peel 1 potato?

_____ minutes

This graph shows the results of the bottom team in the league. From the 40 games Atrocious City won _____,

lost _____,

drew _____ .

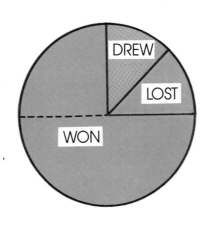

Results
for
Atrocious
City
(40 games)

 This is the graph for the top team. From the 40 games Wonderhampton won _____,

lost _____,

drew _____ .

Results
for
Wonderhampton
Rovers
(40 games)

 This is a graph of Mary's journey which started from her home. She ran, rested for a while and then walked.

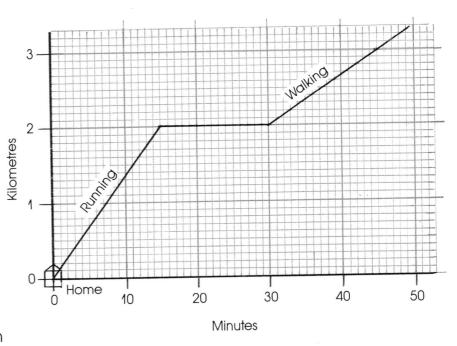

How far from home was Mary after:

15 min? _____ km

20 min? _____ km

30 min? _____ km

 After how many minutes was she

3 km from home? _____   1 km from home? _____

Chance

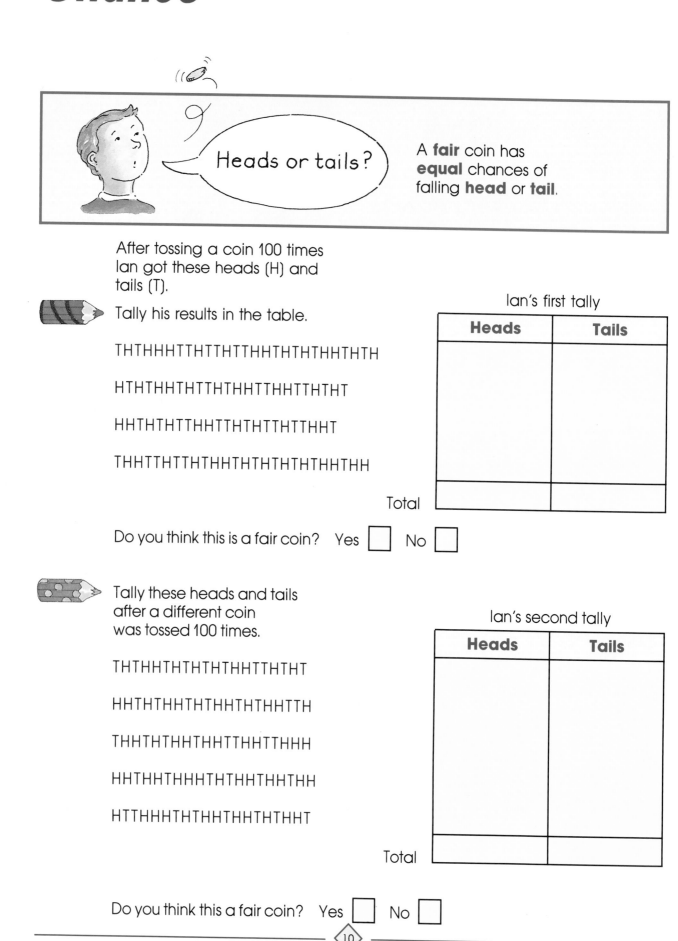

Heads or tails?

A **fair** coin has **equal** chances of falling **head** or **tail**.

After tossing a coin 100 times Ian got these heads (H) and tails (T).

Tally his results in the table.

THTHHHTTHTTHTTHHTHTHTHTHHHTHTH

HTHTHHTHTTHTHHHTTHHTTHTHT

HHTHTHTTHHTTHTHTTHTTHHT

THHTTHTTHTHHTHTHTHTHTHHHTHH

Ian's first tally	
Heads	**Tails**
Total	

Do you think this is a fair coin?   Yes ☐   No ☐

Tally these heads and tails after a different coin was tossed 100 times.

THTHHHTHTHTHTHHTTHTHT

HHTHTHHHTHTHHTHTHHHTTH

THHTHTHHTHHTTHHTTHHH

HHTHHTHHHHTHTHHTHHTHH

HTTHHHHTHTHHTHHHTHTHHHT

Ian's second tally	
Heads	**Tails**
Total	

Do you think this a fair coin?   Yes ☐   No ☐

If a fair coin is tossed 200 times:

how many times should it fall **heads**? ☐

how many times should it fall **tails**? ☐

If a fair coin is tossed 2000 times:

how many times should it fall **heads**? ☐

how may times should it fall **tails**? ☐

This is a fair dice numbered
1, 2, 3, 4, 5, 6.

The dice was rolled 120 times.

Finish the totals in this table.

Score	1	2	3	4	5	6
Tally	ЦНІ ЦНІ ЦНІ ЦНІ І	ЦНІ ЦНІ ЦНІ ІІІІ	ЦНІ ЦНІ ЦНІ ЦНІ	ЦНІ ЦНІ ЦНІ ІІІІ	ЦНІ ЦНІ ЦНІ ЦНІ І	ЦНІ ЦНІ ЦНІ ЦНІ
Total number of times scored	21					

Another dice numbered

1, 2, 3, 4, 5, 6

was rolled 120 times.
A graph of the results was drawn.

How many times was the score:

1? ☐   2? ☐

3? ☐   4? ☐

5? ☐   6? ☐

Is this a fair dice?   Yes ☐   No ☐

Graph of scores

Number of times scored vs Score

Tenths and hundredths

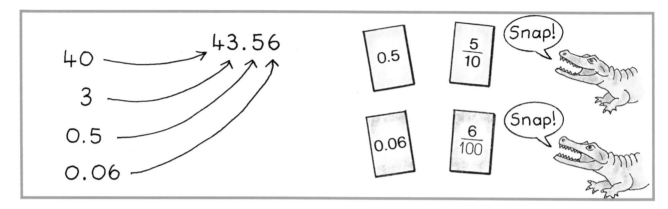

 Write these fractions as decimals.

$\frac{1}{10}$ = __O.____ $\frac{2}{10}$ = __O.____ $\frac{3}{10}$ = _____

$\frac{4}{10}$ = _____ $\frac{5}{10}$ = _____ $\frac{6}{10}$ = _____

$\frac{7}{10}$ = _____ $\frac{8}{10}$ = _____ $\frac{9}{10}$ = _____

$\frac{1}{100}$ = __O.O____ $\frac{7}{100}$ = _____ $\frac{3}{100}$ = _____

$\frac{9}{100}$ = _____ $\frac{2}{100}$ = _____ $\frac{8}{100}$ = _____

 Write down the decimal shown by each arrow on this number line.

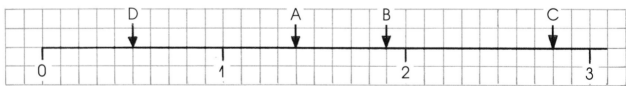

A is _1._   B is ____   C is ____   D is ____

 On the number line below mark:

A↓ 0.3 ✓   B↓ 0.7   C↓ 0.6

D↓ 0.03   E↓ 0.07   F↓ 0.16

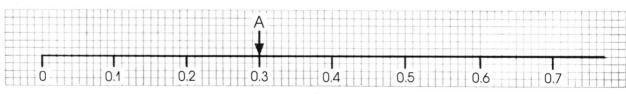

On the number line below mark:

P↓   0.25   Q↓   0.75   R↓   0.35

X↓   0.62   Y↓   0.69   Z↓   0.48

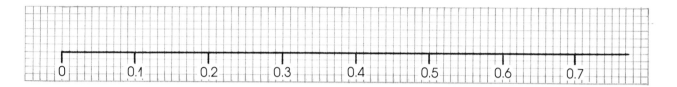

0   0.1   0.2   0.3   0.4   0.5   0.6   0.7

 Use the number lines to help you answer these questions.

Which decimal is halfway between 1 and 2?   `1.`

Which decimal is halfway between 1.4 and 1.6?   ☐

Which decimal is halfway between 1.3 and 1.9?   ☐

Do these additions and subtractions.

0.2 +0.9 ———	0.3 +0.8 ———	£0.40 +£0.70 ——— £	£0.50 +£0.60 ——— £
1.25 +0.25 ———	1.35 +0.15 ———	£0.54 +£0.67 ——— £	£1.33 +£1.48 ——— £
0.9 −0.4 ———	1.4 −0.9 ———	£1.30 −£0.80 ——— £	£1.40 −£0.90 ——— £
2.25 −1.06 ———	2.25 −0.06 ———	£2.25 −£1.16 ——— £	£2.25 −£0.26 ——— £

Which is greater 0.2 or 0.07?   ☐

Which is greater 0.25 or 0.3?   ☐

Is 0.6 greater than, less than or equal to ⅗?   ☐

Fractions

Tammy's piece
$\frac{1}{4}$

Tom's piece
$\frac{1}{4}$

For Mary and Ian
$\frac{1}{2}$

HAPPY BIRTHDAY

 Put the missing fractions in these sentences.

Tammy and Tom together will have ☐ of the cake.

Tammy, Mary and Ian together will have ☐ of the cake.

When Tom takes his piece first there will be ☐ left.

 Colour ½ of this square.   Colour ¼ of this one.   Colour ¾ of this one.

 Write the missing fractions on these charts.

1			
		$\frac{1}{4}$	

1			
$\frac{1}{5}$			
			$\frac{2}{10}$	

 Use the charts to help you fill in these boxes.

$\frac{1}{2} = \frac{\Box}{10}$ $\frac{4}{10} = \frac{\Box}{5}$ $\frac{2}{4} = \frac{\Box}{2}$

$\frac{3}{5} = \frac{\Box}{10}$ $\frac{8}{10} = \frac{\Box}{5}$ $\frac{2}{10} = \frac{\Box}{5}$

$1 = \frac{\Box}{4}$ $1 = \frac{\Box}{10}$ $1 = \frac{\Box}{5}$

Do these additions.

$\frac{1}{4} + \frac{1}{2} =$ $\frac{3}{4} + \frac{1}{4} =$ $\frac{3}{4} + \frac{3}{4} =$

$\frac{1}{5} + \frac{3}{5} =$ $\frac{2}{5} + \frac{3}{5} =$ $\frac{3}{5} + \frac{3}{5} =$

$\frac{3}{10} + \frac{3}{10} =$ $\frac{3}{10} + \frac{7}{10} =$ $\frac{3}{10} + \frac{8}{10} =$

 Do these subtractions.

$\frac{3}{4} - \frac{1}{2} =$ $\frac{7}{10} - \frac{4}{10} =$ $\frac{3}{5} - \frac{2}{5} =$

$1 - \frac{1}{4} =$ $1 - \frac{3}{5} =$ $1\frac{3}{5} - \frac{1}{5} =$

$1\frac{1}{2} - \frac{3}{4} =$ $1\frac{1}{4} - \frac{3}{4} =$ $1\frac{2}{5} - \frac{4}{5} =$

Eighths

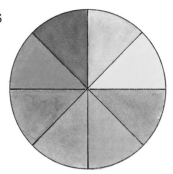

Change these fractions to ⅛ths.

$\frac{1}{2} = \dfrac{\Box}{8}$ $\frac{1}{4} = \dfrac{\Box}{8}$ $\frac{3}{4} = \dfrac{\Box}{8}$

Is $\frac{5}{8}$ greater than $\frac{1}{2}$? _____

Is $\frac{5}{8}$ less than $\frac{3}{4}$? _____

Fill in the missing numbers.

$\frac{1}{2} = \dfrac{\Box}{4} = \dfrac{\Box}{8}$ $\frac{1}{2} = \dfrac{\Box}{4} = \dfrac{\Box}{10}$ $\frac{4}{4} = \dfrac{\Box}{8} = \dfrac{\Box}{10}$

Work these out.

$\frac{3}{5} + \frac{3}{10} = \dfrac{\Box}{10}$ $\frac{2}{5} + \frac{1}{2} = \dfrac{\Box}{10}$ $\frac{1}{5} + \frac{7}{10} = \dfrac{\Box}{10}$

$\frac{1}{2} + \frac{3}{8} = \dfrac{\Box}{8}$ $\frac{1}{4} + \frac{3}{8} = \dfrac{\Box}{8}$ $\frac{1}{8} + \frac{3}{4} = \dfrac{\Box}{8}$

Use $<$ for **less than**, $>$ for **more than** and $=$ for **equal to**.

$\frac{1}{4} < \frac{1}{2}$ $\frac{3}{4} > \frac{1}{4}$ $\frac{2}{4} = \frac{1}{2}$

Put $<$, $>$ or $=$ in each box to make these correct.

$\frac{1}{2} \Box \frac{5}{10}$ $\frac{1}{2} \Box \frac{2}{5}$ $\frac{1}{2} \Box \frac{3}{5}$

$\frac{1}{4} \Box \frac{3}{10}$ $\frac{1}{4} \Box \frac{2}{10}$ $\frac{2}{4} \Box \frac{1}{2}$

$\frac{4}{10} \Box \frac{2}{5}$ $\frac{5}{10} \Box \frac{3}{4}$ $\frac{5}{10} \Box \frac{4}{5}$

Grids and scales

Fred

I am ½ as long, ½ as high and ½ as wide as Fred.

Fred's friend

? cm

? cm

 Measure the length of Fred. _____ cm

Measure the length of Fred's friend. _____ cm

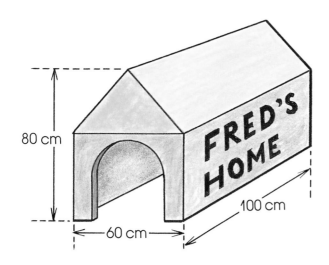

80 cm

60 cm

100 cm

FRED'S HOME

Fred's friend needs a kennel which is ½ as long as Fred's.

 Fill in the measurements for the new kennel.
Keep it the same shape as Fred's.

Length _____ cm

Width _____ cm

Height _____ cm

 Write down the pair of coordinates for each corner of Fred's garden.

A is (1 , __)   B is (7 , __)

C is (__ , __)   D is (__ , __)

E is (__ , __)   F is (__ , __)

 With a scale 1cm represents 1m:

the scale length of AB is ___ cm,

the real length of AB is ___ m.

Scale: 1cm represents 1m

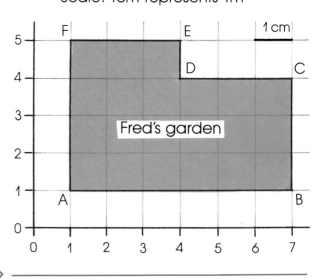

Fred's garden

the scale length of BC is ___ cm, the real length is ___ m.

the scale length of AF is ___ cm, the real length is ___ m.

the scale length of FE is ___ cm, the real length is ___ m.

the scale length of ED is ___ cm, the real length is ___ m.

 On the scale drawing of Fred's garden (ABCDEF)

the perimeter is ___ cm,

the real perimeter is ___ metres.

 On the scale drawing the area is ___ square cm,

the real area is ___ square metres.

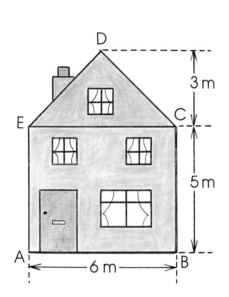

This is a sketch of the house of Fred's owner.

 Draw a plan of the house.

Use a scale: 1cm represents 1 metre.

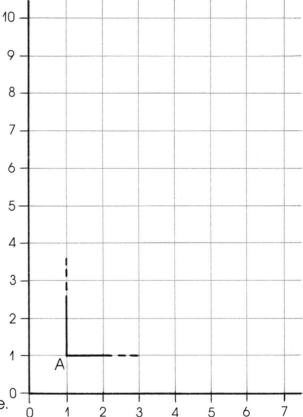

A is the point (1,1) on your plan.
Which pair of coordinates represents:

B? (__, __)   C? (__, __)   D? (__, __)

 Count squares and parts of squares to find the area of the front of the house.

Scale area = _____ square cm

Real area = _____ square m

Adding and subtracting

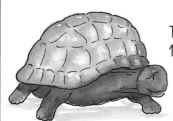

The tortoise is
102 years old.

Ian is
9 years old.

$102 + 9 = 111$ The ages add up to 111 years.

$102 - 9 = 93$ The difference in ages is 93 years.

 Adding and subtracting will help you to answer these.

15 years ago the tortoise was _____ years old.

In 15 years time Ian will be _____ years old.

 Finish these addition trains.

$$
\begin{array}{c}
27 \\
+\ 27 \\
\hline
54
\end{array}
\qquad
\begin{array}{c}
54 \\
+\ 27 \\
\hline
\end{array}
\qquad
\begin{array}{c}
\\
+\ 27 \\
\hline
\end{array}
\qquad
\begin{array}{c}
\\
+\ 27 \\
\hline
\end{array}
\qquad
\begin{array}{c}
\\
+\ 27 \\
\hline
\end{array}
$$

$$
\begin{array}{c}
103 \\
+103 \\
\hline
\end{array}
\qquad
\begin{array}{c}
\\
+\ 103 \\
\hline
\end{array}
\qquad
\begin{array}{c}
\\
+\ 103 \\
\hline
\end{array}
\qquad
\begin{array}{c}
\\
+\ 103 \\
\hline
\end{array}
\qquad
\begin{array}{c}
\\
+\ 103 \\
\hline
\end{array}
$$

$$
\begin{array}{c}
233 \\
+\ 233 \\
\hline
\end{array}
\qquad
\begin{array}{c}
\\
+\ 233 \\
\hline
\end{array}
\qquad
\begin{array}{c}
\\
+\ 233 \\
\hline
\end{array}
\qquad
\begin{array}{c}
\\
+\ 233 \\
\hline
\end{array}
\qquad
\begin{array}{c}
\\
+\ 233 \\
\hline
\end{array}
$$

$$
\begin{array}{c}
209 \\
+\ 209 \\
\hline
\end{array}
\qquad
\begin{array}{c}
\\
+\ 209 \\
\hline
\end{array}
\qquad
\begin{array}{c}
\\
+\ 209 \\
\hline
\end{array}
\qquad
\begin{array}{c}
\\
+\ 209 \\
\hline
\end{array}
\qquad
\begin{array}{c}
\\
+\ 209 \\
\hline
\end{array}
$$

Fill in these addition squares. Add ⟷   Add

26	27	28	81
25	27	29	
24	27	30	
			243

43	42	41	
44	44	44	
45	46	47	

55	54	53	
54	55	53	
53	54	55	

Finish these subtraction trains.

```
  999             777
− 222           − 222           − 222           − 222
─────           ─────           ─────           ─────
  777
─────           ─────           ─────           ─────
```

```
  902
− 106           − 106           − 106           − 106
─────           ─────           ─────           ─────
```

```
  795
− 131           − 131           − 131           − 131
─────           ─────           ─────           ─────
```

```
  896
− 224           − 224           − 224           − 224
─────           ─────           ─────           ─────
```

Work out these addition and subtraction sums.

```
  1573            1357            1375            1735
+  297          +  297          +  297          +  297
──────          ──────          ──────          ──────
```

```
  1573            1357            1375            1735
−  297          −  297          −  297          −  297
──────          ──────          ──────          ──────
```

Length

This line is 1 cm long.

This piece of string is about 1 metre long.

100 cm = 1 metre

1000 metres = 1 kilometre

 Ian cut 17 cm of string from a 1 metre length.

What length did Ian leave? _____ cm

Mary cut 25 cm from the piece left.

What length did Mary leave? _____ cm

May has to run 1 kilometre.

After 1 minute she has run 190 metres.

How much further has she to run? _____ metres

In the second minute May runs 210 metres.

May still has to run _____ metres.

Change these lengths to centimetres.

1 m 50 cm = _____ cm   1 m 5 cm = _____ cm

¼ metre = _____ cm   ¹⁄₁₀ metre = _____ cm

 Change these lengths to metres.

1 km 500 m = _____ m   1 km 50 m = _____ m

1 km 5 m = _____ m   ½ kilometre = _____ m

2½ km = _____ m   ¹⁄₁₀ kilometre = _____ m

¹⁄₁₀₀ km = _____ m   ¹⁄₁₀₀₀ km = _____ m

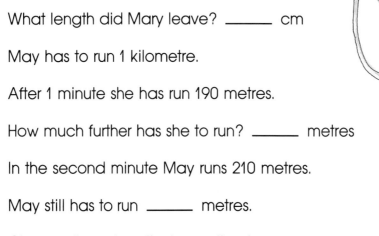

Work out the answers to these sums.

m	cm
2	75
+1	75

m	cm
5	30
−2	55

m	cm
1	30
	×4

1 metre ÷ 5

= _____ cm

km	m
2	600
+1	500

km	m
3	400
−1	600

km	m
1	500
	×4

1 km ÷ 5

= _____ m

km	m
3	750
+1	340

km	m
4	260
−1	360

km	m
2	250
	×4

2 km ÷ 4

= _____ m

This graph shows the distance travelled by a cyclist.

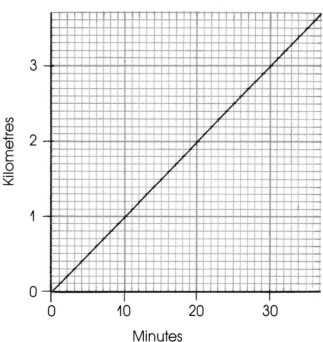

Use the graph to help you
work out the distance
travelled in:

10 minutes _____ km,

20 minutes _____ km,

30 minutes _____ km,

15 minutes _____ km,

25 minutes _____ km.

My car is either 400 cm long or 40 m long.

Which length is it? _____

How many centimetres make 1 kilometre? _____

Percentages

10% is read as **ten per cent**.

10% means **10** per **100**
which is $\frac{10}{100} = \frac{1}{10}$ or 0.1.

 Fill in the fractions and decimals for these percentages.

Percentage	Fraction	Decimal
10%	$\frac{10}{100} = \frac{\Box}{10}$	0.1
20%	$\frac{20}{100} = \frac{\Box}{10}$	0.2
30%		
40%		
50%		
60%		
70%		
80%		
90%		

A **cent**urion was
a Roman soldier.

He had **100** men
under his command.

For the centurion:

50 of his 100 men will be _____ % or $\frac{50}{100} = \frac{1}{2}$,

25 of his 100 men will be _____ % or $\frac{\square}{100} = \frac{\square}{4}$,

75 of his 100 men will be _____ % or $\boxed{} = \boxed{}$.

 From the centurion's 100 soldiers how many will be:

10% ? $\boxed{}$ 15% ? $\boxed{}$ 60% ? $\boxed{}$

Work out these percentages for an army of 200 soldiers.

50% of 200 = $\frac{50}{100}$ of 200   25% of 200 =

$= \frac{1}{2}$ of 200   =

=   =

75% of 200   10% of 200

=   =

A grocer finds that 10% of his tomatoes are bad.

 How many will be bad in:

a box of 100? $\boxed{}$ a box of 200? $\boxed{}$

a box of 1000? $\boxed{}$ a box of 2000? $\boxed{}$

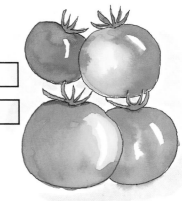

Colour 50% of each rectangle in red,

    25% in blue, 10% in green

and 5% in black.

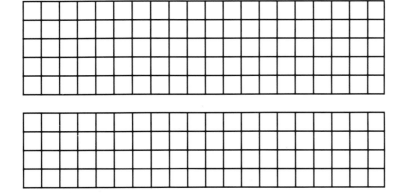

Weight

This is a graph of the weights of Ann, Tom and Emma.

 Fill in this table.

Ann _____ kg

Tom _____ kg

Emma _____ kg

Total _____ kg

 Divide the weight by 3 to find the average weight of the 3 children.

_____ kg

By how much is Ann heavier than Emma? _____ kg

By how much is Tom lighter than Ann? _____ kg

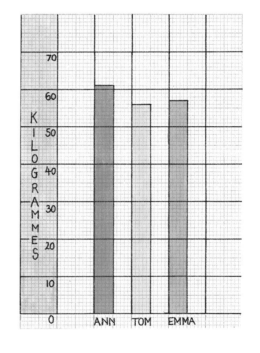

 Write down the answers.

500g × 4 = _____ kg   500g × 10 = _____ kg

2kg 500g × 2 = _____ kg   2kg 250g × 4 = _____ kg

250g ÷ 5 = _____ g   1kg 250g ÷ 5 = _____ g

1½kg ÷ 3 = _____ g   2½kg ÷ 5 = _____ g

This is a graph of the weight of litter collected on a sponsored 'clean-up'.

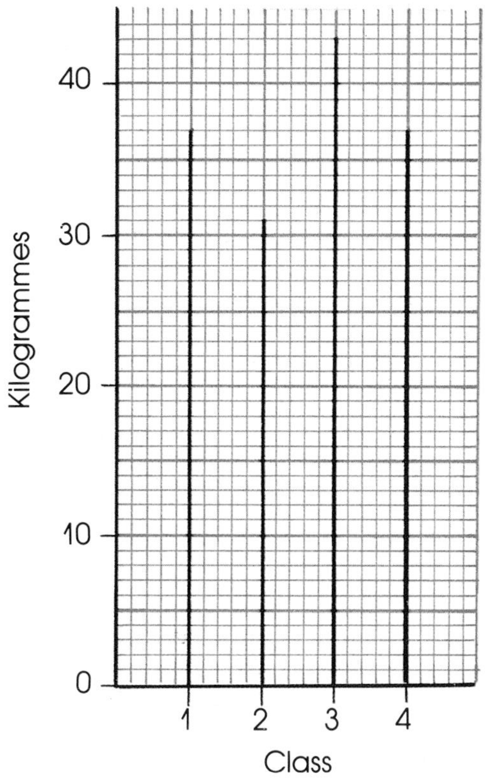

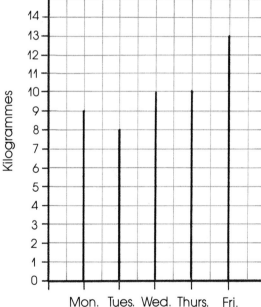

What weight was collected by:

Class 1? _____ kg

Class 2? _____ kg

Class 3? _____ kg

Class 4? _____ kg

The total collected was _____ kg.

What was the average weight collected?

_____ kg

At £2.50 per kg collected how much was raised from sponsors by:

Class 1? £ _____   Class 2? £ _____

Class 3? £ _____   Class 4? £ _____

This graph shows the weight of sweets sold in the school tuck-shop.

Which day had the:

highest sale? _____

lowest sale? _____

What was the total sale for the week?

_____ kg

_____ kg

_____ kg

_____ kg

_____ kg

Total _____ kg

What was the average daily weight sold? _____ kg

At £4.50 per kg what were the takings on Monday? £ _____

Area and volume

I take up more space than you do.

Write down the number of square centimetres covered by each shape.

Shape	Square cm
1	
2	
3	
4	
5	
6	
7	

Which one of the shapes covers the most area?   Number _____

Which one of the shapes covers the least area?   Number _____

Which shapes have an area of:

7 square cm? _____ , _____ , _____   8 square cm? _____ , _____

On this grid of cm squares draw:

1 a square with area **16** square cm.

2 a square with area **9** square cm.

3 a rectangle **3** squares wide with an area of **15** square cm.

4 a rectangle with area **21** square cm.

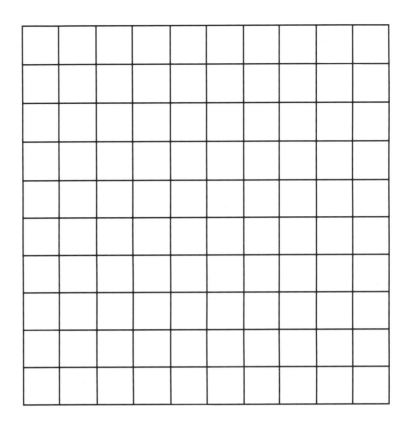

The space in this box is to be filled with 1 cm cubes.

 How many cubes will fit on the bottom?

_____ cubes

How many cubes will fill the box?

_____ cubes

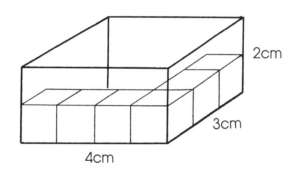

2cm

3cm

4cm

How many 1 cm cubes will fill each of these boxes?

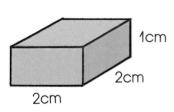

1cm

2cm

2cm

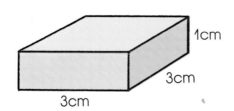

1cm

3cm

3cm

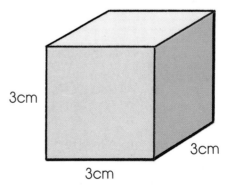

3cm

3cm

3cm

_____ cubes   _____ cubes   _____ cubes

Shapes and angles

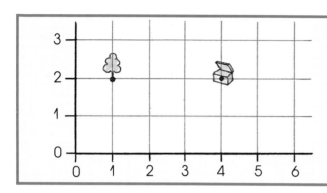

The tree is at the point with coordinates (1,2).

You must dig for treasure at point (4,2).

 Join point **B** to point (1,7).

Join point **A** to point (1,7).

What shape have you drawn?

_____

What is the name of the angle you have made at **B**?

_____

How many degrees is the angle at **B**?

_____

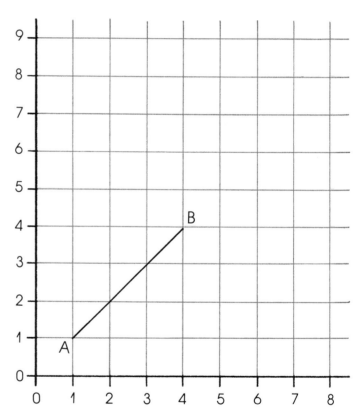

 Now start at (4,0) and draw a line parallel to line **AB** and the same length as **AB**.

Where does your line finish?   (____ , ____)

 Join these points in order:

(3,6) ⟶ (7,6) ⟶ (8,8) ⟶ (4,8) ⟶ (3,6).

What is the name of the shape you have drawn? _____

Which one of these angles is called:

acute?   Number _____

obtuse?   Number _____

reflex?   Number _____

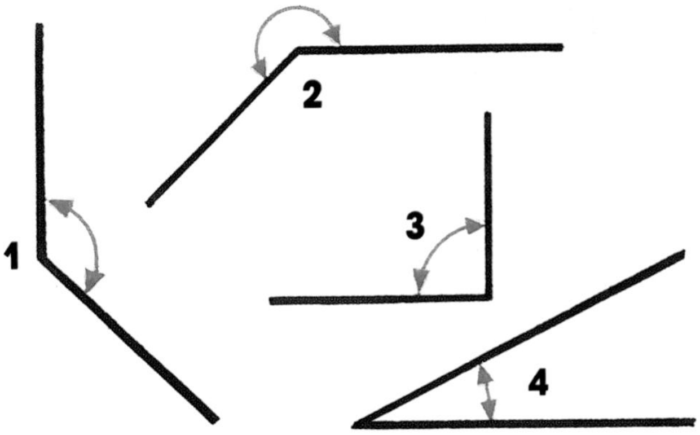

1

2

3

4

Draw these shapes full size and as accurately as you can.

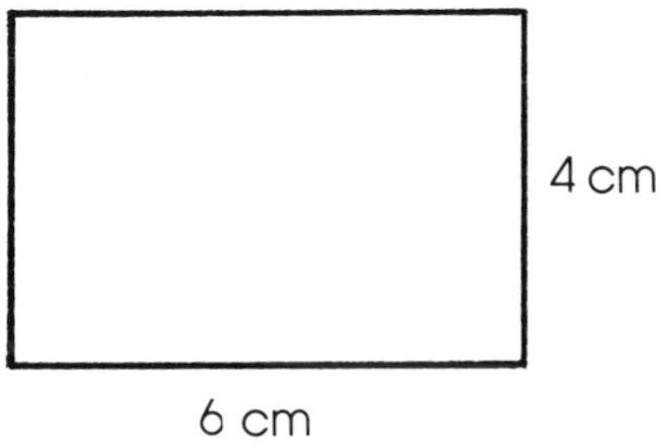

4 cm

6 cm

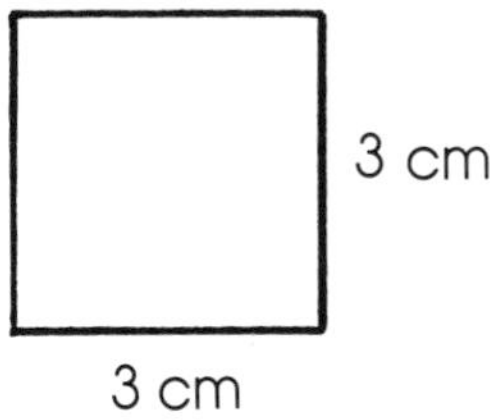

3 cm

3 cm

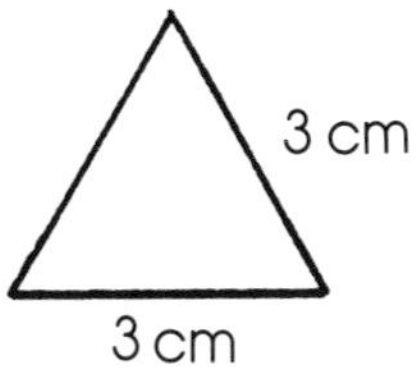

3 cm

3 cm

This line | is a line of symmetry for each road sign.

Finish drawing the road signs.

Calculation

Ian did this division.

$$\frac{1}{5} = 1 \div 5 = 0.2$$

Mary tried this one but couldn't seem to finish it.

$$\frac{1}{3} = 1 \div 3 = 0.333333$$

 Check Ian's sum on a calculator.

$$1 \div 5 = \underline{\hspace{2cm}}$$

 Check Mary's sum on a calculator.

$$1 \div 3 = \underline{\hspace{2cm}}$$

Mary's aunt had her lunch and counted the calories.

 Total the calories for Mary's aunt.

Calorie count	Calories
1 boiled egg	85
2 slices of bread	135
butter	54
2 cups of coffee	65
1 small cake	77
Total	☐

 Change these fractions to decimals.

$$\frac{1}{2} = \qquad \frac{1}{4} = \qquad \frac{3}{4} =$$

$$\frac{1}{10} = \qquad \frac{7}{10} = \qquad \frac{3}{10} =$$

$$\frac{1}{5} = \qquad \frac{2}{5} = \qquad \frac{3}{5} =$$

 Do these sums without a calculator and then check your answer with a calculator.

$$424 \div 8 = \underline{\hspace{1.5cm}} \qquad 420 \div 8 = \underline{\hspace{1.5cm}} \qquad 480 \div 80 = \underline{\hspace{1.5cm}}$$

631 × 5 = _____   632 × 5 = _____   633 × 5 = _____

723 ÷ 3 = _____   723 ÷ 30 = _____   72.3 ÷ 3 = _____

420 × 6 = _____   42 × 60 = _____   420 × 60 = _____

75 × 4 ÷ 3 = _____   56 × 9 ÷ 7 = _____

9 × 9 × 9 = _____   11 × 11 × 11 = _____

 Check these patterns and write the next two lines of each one.
Check by using a calculator.

1 × 9 + 2 = $\boxed{11}$ 37037 × 6 = $\boxed{222222}$

12 × 9 + 3 = $\boxed{111}$ 37037 × 9 = $\boxed{333333}$

123 × 9 + 4 = $\boxed{}$ 37037 × 12 = $\boxed{}$

$\boxed{}$ × 9 + $\boxed{}$ = $\boxed{}$ $\boxed{}$ × $\boxed{}$ = $\boxed{}$

1 × 1   = $\boxed{1}$ 33 × 37 = $\boxed{1221}$

11 × 11   = $\boxed{121}$ 333 × 37 = $\boxed{12321}$

111 × 111 = $\boxed{}$ $\boxed{}$ × 37 = $\boxed{}$

$\boxed{}$ × $\boxed{}$ = $\boxed{}$ $\boxed{}$ × $\boxed{}$ = $\boxed{}$

  Answer these puzzles. Use a calculator if you need to.

Ian thinks of a number, doubles it, adds 5
and gets the answer 25. What was Ian's number? $\boxed{}$

Mary thinks of a number, halves it, adds 5
and gets the answer 10. What was her number? $\boxed{}$

Which number multiplied by itself and then by 2 becomes 98? $\boxed{}$

Which is the lowest number divisible by 3, 5 and 7? $\boxed{}$

Which is the lowest number divisible by 4, 8 and 9? $\boxed{}$

31

Answers

To Parents: We have not provided *all* the answers here. We suggest that items to be drawn should be checked by you. In the case of activities where calculations are performed by your child, it would be good practice to get him/her to use a calculator to check the answers.

Page 2

8 4 2
8 4

31 63

1110 1000 1000 1030

202 98 363 198

Page 3

193 411 380 701 600

201 199 209 241 251

301 122 245 44
99 278 155 356

6 4 5 5
5 7 7 6

7 6 6 7
4 4 7 6

Page 4

3000 4500 6000 7500

3000
3000 6000
4500 9000
6000

7500 9000 10500 12000
375 378 738 1110

Page 5

1845 1424 2100 1791

×	1	2	3	4	5	6	7	8	9	10
1	1	2	3	4	5	6	7	8	9	10
2	2	4	6	8	10	12	14	16	18	20
3	3	6	9	12	15	18	21	24	27	30
4	4	8	12	16	20	24	28	32	36	40
5	5	10	15	20	25	30	35	40	45	50
6	6	12	18	24	30	36	42	48	54	60
7	7	14	21	28	35	42	49	56	63	70
8	8	16	24	32	40	48	56	64	72	80
9	9	18	27	36	45	54	63	72	81	90
10	10	20	30	40	50	60	70	80	90	100

860 2160 1827 747
1836 1476 4527 2919

Page 6

24 48 12 6 4 40

21 28 14 12
210 168 140 120
420 280 105 84
402 268 134 68

Page 7

25 12,2 8,2
250,0 125,0 83,2
5,0 6,2 16,2
50,0 62,4 166,2

Page 7 (cont)

9
5
2,4,7
2,3,4,6,8,12
2,3,4,6,9,12,18
1,29

55 45,5 39,2
51,3 126,2 112,4
106,4 99 101,1

Page 8

8 12
10 6
20 60 2

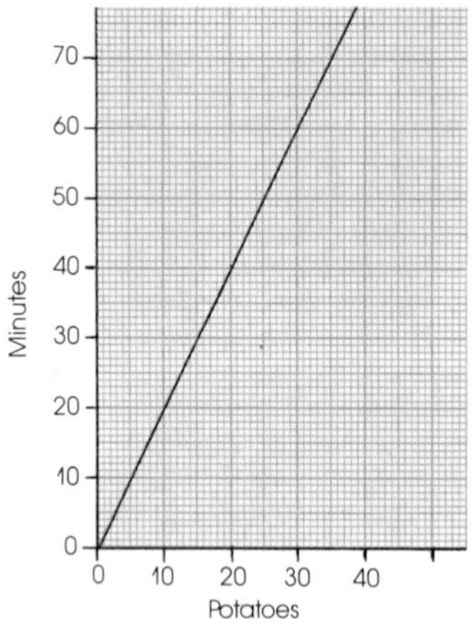

Minutes
0
10
20
30
40
50
60
70
0
10
20
30
40
Potatoes

Page 9

10 20 10
30 5 5

2 2 2
45 7½

Page 10

First tally : heads : 51, tails : 49
Yes
Second tally : heads : 60, tails : 40
No

Page 11

100 100 1000 1000

Score: 2 3 4 5 6
Total 19 20 19 21 20

20 21
20 16
27 16
No

Page 12

0.1 0.2 0.3
0.4 0.5 0.6
0.7 0.8 0.9
0.01 0.07 0.03
0.09 0.02 0.08

1.4 1.9 2.8 0.5

Page 12 (cont)

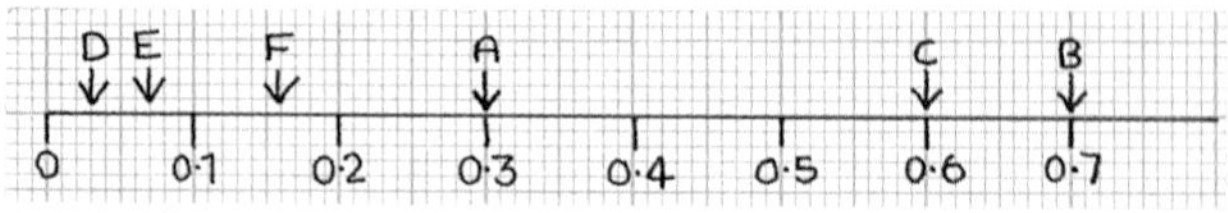

D
E
F
A
C
B
0
0·1
0·2
0·3
0·4
0·5
0·6
0·7

Page 13

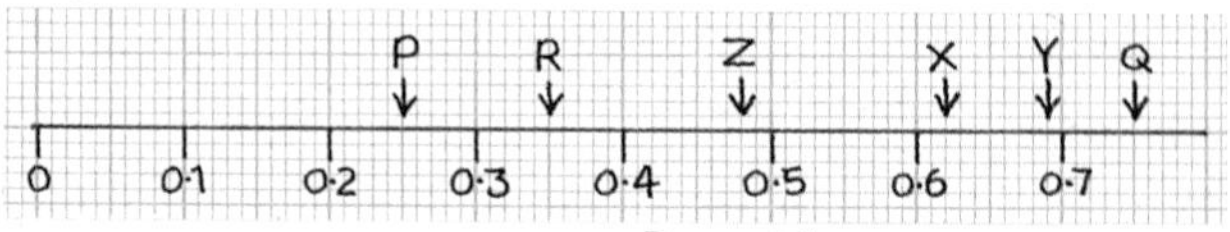

P
R
Z
X
Y
Q
0
0·1
0·2
0·3
0·4
0·5
0·6
0·7

1.5 1.5 1.6

1.1 1.1 1.10 1.10
1.5 1.5 1.21 2.81
0.5 0.5 0.50 0.50
1.19 2.19 1.09 1.99

0.2 0.3 equal to

Page 14

½ ¾ ¾

Colour ½ = 8 squares
Colour ¼ = 4 squares
Colour ¾ = 12 squares

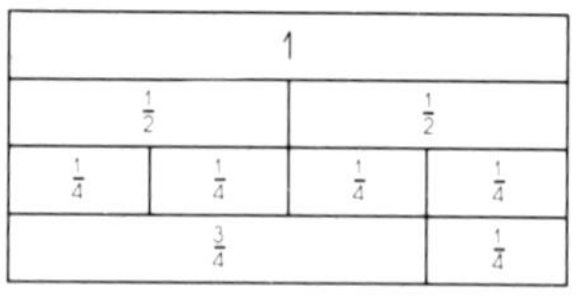

1
½
½
¼
¼
¼
¼
¾
¼

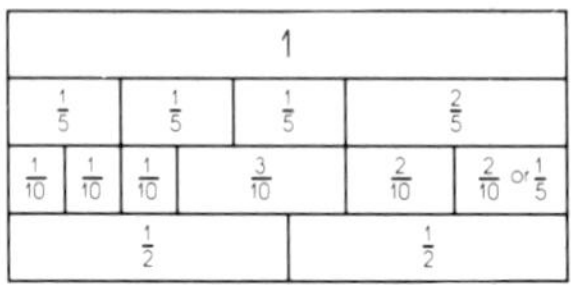

1
⅕
⅕
⅕
⅖
1/10
1/10
1/10
3/10
2/10
2/10 or ⅕
½
½

5 2 1
6 4 1
4 10 5

Page 15

¾ 1 1½
⅘ 1 1⅕
⅗ 1 1 1/10

¼ 3/10 ⅕
¾ ⅖ 1⅖
¾ ½ ⅗

4 2 6
Yes Yes

2,4 2,5 8,10

9 9 9
7 5 7
= > <
< > =
= < <

Page 16

6 3
50 30 40

1 1
7,4 4,4
4,5 1,5

6 6

Page 17

3 3
4 4
3 3
1 1
20 20
21 21

7,1 7,6 4,9
39 39

Page 18

87 24

81 108 135
81 108 135 162

206 309 412 515
206 309 412 515 618

466 699 932 1165
466 699 932 1165 1398

418 627 836 1045
418 627 836 1045 1254

Page 19

81
81
75 81 87

126
132
138
132 132 132 396

162
162
162
162 163 161 486

555 333
555 333 111

796 690 584
796 690 584 478

664 533 402
664 533 402 271

672 448 224
672 448 224 0